Know what? You're in a vicious circle

When you feel low, you tend to stop doing things. You don't go out so much, you avoid seeing friends and you even stop listening to music or watching sport.
As a result, you feel even lower, and then you feel like doing even less. It's like: the less you do, the worse you feel, the worse you feel, the less you do. And it keeps going round and round and round…

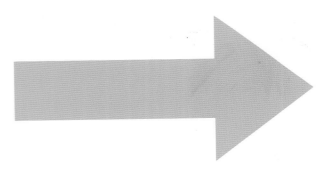

Good News -
you can break the circle!

WOW!

Do you know
what you just did?

V GOOD

You broke the circle

All it took was a little bit of positive action - turning that page.
Now all you have to do is take another tiny step, then another and another.
What steps? That's what this book is about – to show you the easy steps you can take to break that circle into bits and start feeling better.

So here's what you do next

Fill in your diary

Write down everything you do in the next few days. Include things like getting dressed, talking to a friend on the phone, washing your hair, etc. Then score them out of ten for pleasure, achievement and feeling close to other people. The first few spaces are filled in to show you how to do it.

Doing this will help you understand what's good in your life and also to realise what's missing.

About closeness

Feeling close to others is really important, but when we're down, we sometimes hide away. If your diary doesn't have enough things with a good closeness score, this book will help you sort that out.

	Pleasure	Achievement	Closeness
Talking to Alison on the phone	9	3	10
Cleaning the house	1	10	0
Went for a meal with Maria	7	9	8
Spoke to Di on the phone	9	7	10
Bought some wool	6	9	
Went to Lesley's	9	9	9

	Pleasure	Achievement	Closeness
Went to Bethany	8	10	7
Went away for 3 days	6	7	6
Sorted out my winter clothes	8	9	7
Washed my hair	7	8	6
Prayed with Maria	8	9	10
Went to coffee morning	6	8	9

ANYTHING MISSING FROM YOUR DIARY?

Are you ignoring important things?

Paying the bills, looking after yourself, keeping up with the housework - they can all seem too much trouble when you're down.

The problem is, avoiding these essentials makes you feel worse and can get you in a mess. So here's what to do: choose one thing that wasn't in your diary but should have been, and do it - now.

Pay that bill. Make that call. Get your hair done. Do some tidying. Wash the dishes.

You'll feel loads better afterwards and you'll be able to add it to your diary and put a 10 in the 'achievement' box!

FIND SOMETHING TO GET UP FOR

Rebuild your routine

Having to get out of bed to walk the dog or feed the baby can be a real pain, especially on cold mornings, but it's also a great way to feel better.

No dog? No baby? Then make yourself a routine with other things. Shaving and showering. Cleaning the house. Popping to the corner shop to say hello and buy some bacon and eggs. Cooking them for breakfast! Can't get out? Make the most of activities you can do.

And if you rebuild your routine with things that involve others (ringing your mum each morning, walking with a friend every Wednesday) you'll feel even better because of that closeness thing we mentioned before.

It needs to be a daily routine, too. Choose something every single day that you need to get up and out of bed for. Don't lie in - remember, the less you do the worse you feel, the worse you feel, the less you do.

Now make a list of the things you enjoy

Check your diary and pick out the things you did that scored highly for pleasure or closeness to others. Write them down here.

Seeing Friends

Reading

Knitting

What about things you've stopped doing?

Your diary may not contain all the things you like to do, so have a look through this list and tick the ones that apply to you – stuff you used to enjoy but haven't felt like doing lately.

Enjoying sport ☐

Going out with friends ☑

Listening to music ☐

Watching a film ☐

Throwing parties or going to them ☐

Watching TV ☐

Phoning or texting friends ☐

Gardening/looking after plants ☐

Going for a walk ☐

Doing exercise ☐

Going to a class or club ☐

Playing a musical instrument ☐

Reading a good book ☑

Doing drama ☐

Going to church, mosque, temple or synagogue ☑

Helping other people ☑

Well ticked!

Now we're going to make a plan

Tricia 's

BIG
PLAN

(Write your name in the gap).

One of the reasons we feel worse when we stop
doing things, is the fact that it's usually the things
we like that we avoid first.

No wonder life seems to go down and down!

To start it going up again, you need to pick good
things to fill your day with. Not all the time –
just one thing to start with. So, once you've got
a bit of a routine going, the next step of your
big plan is to look at the lists you just made
and pick one of the things on them.

Pick something that used to give you pleasure,
or a sense of achievement. Or something that
you think is worthwhile or made you feel
close to others.

Just one.

NOW WRITE
IT HERE IN
BIG LETTERS

Going   to   Church

GOOD

You've just written down the thing you're going to
start doing again.

DON'T WORRY

You're not going to do it all at once!

Instead, you're going to break it into tiny pieces
and do them one by one, in easy steps.

How?

Have a look at the example opposite.

For example

Jack used to like meeting his friends for a walk in the park, but since he's been fed up, he hasn't had the energy for it. This is what he wrote in his plan for getting back to meeting them

1 Go to the park and just sit there enjoying the peace and quiet.

2 Go back to the park and walk by myself. Don't need to talk to anyone if I don't feel like it.

3 Get into the habit of walking by myself 2 or 3 times a week.

4 Get in touch with one friend and arrange to have a walk and a chat.

5 Go to the park with my friend at a time when we're likely to see the others.

6 Arrange to meet the others next time they're walking in the park.

7 Keep going – get into a routine and feel the difference!

Jack knew he could take one step a day, or one step a week, it didn't matter. What mattered was having a plan and making steady progress towards getting some fun back in his life.

Right, that's enough of Jack.
Now back to your plan.

_____Tricia_____'S

BIG PLAN

Write down your chosen activity again here

Going to Church

Now think about the little steps you
can take towards doing it again.
Make them really small and un-scary.
Don't be ambitious, be easy on
yourself. And don't worry if you have
to keep crossing things out, there's
plenty of space.

1. I'm going to get up with Alan in time for church

2. Then I'm going to tidy up

3. Next, I'm going to do the dishes

4. Then I'm going to sit down

5. nesd wednesday I'm going to the prays meeting

6. nesd week I will go to the lunch club

7. going to the lunch club is very pressure

8. Lots of people asking how I am

9. do the pots after the lunch

10. _____

11. _____

12. _____

13. _____

14. _____

15. _____

16. _____

17. _____

18. _____

What if something gets in your way?

As soon as you've written your plan, think about what could stop it happening. Are there any things that might trip you up? What about other people? Could someone be unhelpful at any stage?

When you've figured out what could block your progress, work out another mini-plan for getting round the obstacle. It's called unblocking.

This way, you'll be ready for whatever happens!

A pat on the back

As you do your Big Plan, think about how it helped you feel better or closer to people. Give yourself a pat on the back each evening for the things you have achieved that day.

Make a note of them here.

went out to see Hazel + Philip

got up early

finished reading my book

'S

BIG PLAN

Now check your plan

Is it realistic?

You're not planning to run a marathon are you?

Are you aiming at just one thing?

Don't try and do more than one item on your list. You can always pick another when you've sorted the first one.

Is it slow?

There's no need to rush at things. Your plan can take as long as you like, so long as you stick to it, step by step.

Is it easy?

Make your steps small and easy and you'll be more likely to do them.

Are you ready to unblock it?

Have you thought about what could go wrong and how to deal with it?

Five Ticks? ✓✓✓✓✓
THEN GO FOR IT!

HANG ON!

What if it doesn't work?

Don't worry if you don't finish your plan. Just getting started will be circle-busting, and help you to feel better. If you find that you get stuck halfway through, just sit down and think about why –

- Are the steps too big or hard?
- Would it have been better if you had chosen some other activity?
- Do you need to do a bit of unblocking?

If so, just go back to the beginning of this book, make another plan and have a go at that.
There's no reason to beat yourself up – you're doing great!
You're working on a plan! You deserve a medal!

FOR VALOUR
IN THE FACE OF VICIOUS CIRCLES

WHERE TO GET EVEN MORE HELP

Sometimes, it can seem too difficult to start getting going again, even with small steps.
That's when you need a bit more help than this little book can give.

You can get it at www.livinglifetothefull.com where you'll connect with other people who feel like you, and find out how to contact professionals who can help you make changes to your life.